P9-CAO-120

LOOK WITH EYES OF LOVE

*

By the Same Author

HOUSEHOLD OF FAITH

BE!

HAPPINESS CAN BE A HABIT

PRAYER: THE MASTER KEY

LOOK
*
WITH
*
EYES
*
OF
*
LOVE

James Dillet Freeman

Illustrated by Betty Fraser

DOUBLEDAY & COMPANY, INC.

Garden City, New York

1969

Library of Congress Catalog Card Number 69–15887

Printed in the United States of America
First Edition

Contents

❋

1.

2.

3.

4.

LOOK WITH EYES OF LOVE

*

1

*

How much

How much the human spirit
Outweighs the human pain,
So much that no experience
But can be counted gain!

The unlikely vine

*

There was once a beautiful vineyard. It was the chief joy of the chief gardener. He built a high wall around it, to guard it from the gaze of those who might be tempted to steal some of the grapes and to keep out everything he did not want to let in.

The chief gardener read all the latest books on gardening, and his vinedressers kept all the vines in perfect tilth. They dunged and watered and hoed and pruned the vines according to the most advanced ideas. Nothing was allowed to grow in that garden except the vines the chief gardener set out in his careful rows. Any weed or plant that dared to sprout there quickly found itself in the trash container.

The vines produced as expected. They gave forth bulging, bountiful clusters of luscious, crimson-purple grapes.

The third assistant vinedresser was a young man. "I don't know whether he'll ever amount to much," the chief gardener told his friends. "He's a dreamer, that boy!"

So he was. A great deal of the time he should have been hoeing and pruning, he spent dreaming about better grapes. He also—this the chief gardener did not know—spent a great deal of his time eating the grapes; for he loved to see the grapes growing, but even more he loved the taste of them.

"Grapes," he told his friends, "are to eat!"

One day, he was standing in the vineyard dreaming and eating a bunch of grapes he had just broken off the vine. One by one, he was popping them into his mouth, spitting out the seeds and skin, and savoring the grape meat, when he heard the chief gardener calling him.

Wiping his mouth on his sleeve, he tossed what was left of the grapes over the wall and hurried away.

The bunch of grapes caught in the branches of a bush and fell to the ground. The next spring, where the grapes had fallen, a vine appeared. The spot where the seed had found lodgment was crowded with weeds and scrubby bushes, so the vine had to struggle to stay alive. Worms and beetles gnawed its leaves, which were ragged and yellow and inclined to mildew. But it grew, long, thin, and sprawling.

The little vine pushed up through the bushes, pressing against the wall for support and fastening itself to whatever it could. That winter it rested like all other growing things. The cold winds nipped its tender branches; the frost tried to heave it from the ground. But it survived.

The next spring it began to grow again. It grew to the top of the wall. It grew along the wall. It sent a long stem questing over the wall.

Fortunately the spot it picked was behind a tool shed in the corner, so no one noticed it.

The little vine was happy to be hidden behind the tool shed, for it could see at a glance that it was not like the luxurious vines that grew in the vineyard. The other vines noticed the intruder, however, and they swelled in crimson indignation.

A few of the grapes became so indignant that they burst and their beautiful crimson-purple juice ran down their stems. This made the chief gardener unhappy, but he blamed it on the weather.

"There has been a great deal of rain this summer," said the chief gardener. Even the third assistant vinedresser nodded his head knowingly.

The little vine just kept on quietly growing by itself, and in due season put forth grapes. It bore only one small cluster. The grapes were small, too. They were not at all like the beautiful grapes that grew in the vineyard. They had hardly any color. Even when they ripened, most of them were yellowish or a pale whitish green.

At last it was harvest time and the grapes were gathered. But on the last day of the harvest, the chief gardener, making a final check of things, happened to glance behind the tool shed.

Immediately his glance took in the little vine. He squeezed himself behind the tool shed until he could reach it.

"What a sickly looking little bunch of grapes," he thought, and he swelled with pride as he thought of the huge clusters that grew on his vines.

"We certainly can't have this in our vineyard!" he said, and he tugged at the little vine to uproot it.

But the vine was tough. It had thrust its roots deep into the ground on the other side of the wall and had wrapped its tendrils around branches and twigs. It had grown lithe and strong.

The chief gardener pulled and hauled and wrenched. He snorted and panted and grunted. He ripped off leaves. He broke off stems. He tore off the bunch of grapes.

But the little vine did not give up. It clung to the ground.

It clung to the wall. At last, the chief gardener, sweating and swearing, came stumbling out from behind the tool shed.

His eye lit on the third assistant vinedresser. As usual, he was standing dreaming and eating some grapes alongside one of the vine rows.

"Drop those silly grapes, boy, and come here," roared the chief gardener. "A wild grapevine has somehow grown over the wall. Take a spade and dig it up—and clean up this mess."

Glowering, he walked away.

The third assistant vinedresser cleaned up the litter that the chief gardener had made. The stems and leaves he threw into a trash container, but the little bunch of grapes he kept and began to eat of them as he went to dig up the vine.

He ate one. He ate another.

"I've always heard wild grapes are good," he thought. "These certainly are." He ate another. "Delicious!" Another grape popped into his mouth, and as his teeth closed on the fragrant flesh and the succulent juices began to trickle down his throat, suddenly he became aware that these grapes were not like any grapes he had ever before eaten. He was eating the whole grape! The skin was as soft and delicate as the meat—and there were no seeds!

"There—there are no seeds!" he cried to himself. He plucked another grape from the cluster and tore it open with his teeth. He looked at it. No seeds. No seeds at all.

By this time he had reached the vine.

"The old grouch ordered me to dig it up," he said. "And that's just what I'll do."

That is what he did.

With infinite care he dug up the little vine and carried

it gently to his own cottage. There he planted it, and tended it, and the little vine grew under his loving care. For many years it gave him many grapes and many cuttings, so that in time he had a vineyard for himself.

For the thin-skinned, fragrant little grapes that had no seeds were the best grapes—most people agreed—they had ever eaten.

They became the most famous grapes in all that country, and indeed they became the fame of the country.

The third assistant vinedresser became a rich and famous horticulturist, known far and wide for the goodness of his grapes and the glory of his dreams.

Runners may have blistered feet

Many of us feel like an unlikely vine.

We are not good looking. We do not have much money. Our health is poor. We did not get enough education. We came from the wrong side of the tracks.

But most of the world's work has been done by people who felt ill-equipped to do what they did; they did not have enough brains or education or money or time or strength. Many of them were hungry. Most of them were lonely and afraid, troubled of heart and mind. A few were even desperate.

If we did only the things that we feel ready to do, little that needs doing would ever get done.

We would probably be amazed if we knew how many records have been set by runners who had blistered feet.

As for books that have been written, songs that have been sung, explorations that have been carried out, discoveries that have been made, by people with headaches or stomach-aches—these must be numberless.

Most of the world's work, I imagine, has been done by people who did not much want to do it.

But there the work was to do, so they did it. They even did it well, so well that we may still be benefiting from it and marveling at it.

Of summer webs and weeds

This summer a spider strung a web night after night between two trees behind my house. Every day something tore down the web.

Yet the spider did not make a slipshod web because the web was only going to last a night. It spun a spidery Grand Hotel, dozens of delicate spokes radiating out, criss-crossed by countless glistening strands, a masterwork of arachnidial architecture, of such fragile symmetry that I stopped every morning to look at it. Yet by noon it was gone.

In a crack in my sidewalk I have watched weeds growing. The weeds did not grow halfheartedly because they were growing in a sidewalk crack. They grew as if they had an acre to grow in and as if they knew that heaven and earth were conspiring to bring them to their flowering.

Though I listened many times, I never heard the weeds bewailing their fate or the spider berating its gods.

Most heroes wear no medals

I think of all the people who have done their work because they had it to do.

There are the teachers who have kept on teaching; the wives who have stood by their husbands; the nurses who have kept on tending the sick; the mothers who have given themselves for their children.

There are the lifeguards who take their small boats out into the gales of the world. There are the firemen who keep fighting all the everlasting fires. There are the miners who have gone on digging for the undiscovered gold. There are the explorers who have never given up man's explorations into the unknown.

There are the men who keep at humdrum work until they master a skill or an art—the pianist who plays exercises for hours every day for years until one day at last his exercises are no longer exercises but insights into life; the sounds he makes fall on our hearts and shake us to our silent roots of meaning.

There is the scientist who spends his whole life in a laboratory, peering into a microscope or a telescope or a test tube or an equation, hoping to catch a new glimpse of truth—and perhaps he finds it, or perhaps he does not find it.

There is the student who masters the contents of books so that he can add to what men know.

There are all the soldiers who have done their lonely, dirty, unsung work in the forgotten battle lines and unremembered outposts of men's timeless wars. How many there must have been who knew they were not likely to be coming back from what they had to do—and knew, too, that no one would be there to tell whether they stood or ran. Yet they stood—not because they wanted to, not even because they believed in what they were supposed to be fighting for—but because it was what they had to do.

Most heroes wear no medals.

They are just those who stayed when they wanted to run. They knew that they could run—but they could not hide—not from themselves, or life.

We can go beyond ourselves

This is the greatness of the human being: We can do what we do not want to do, even what we are afraid to do. We can refrain from doing what we do want to do.

We can take charge.

We can go beyond ourselves.

Often we may not want to go.

We are all a little like Ulysses, who pretended to be mad when they called him to leave the wife he loved and his newborn son to fight in the war with Troy as he had promised to do. He yoked an ox and an ass together and feigned plowing his field; but when they laid his son in his path, he turned aside.

Or like Moses, when God came to him where he was keeping sheep in the wilderness and told him he had to go and save his people, most of us begin to think of all the reasons why we cannot go.

But we go.

We may see it is beyond our reach, so we stretch ourselves a little. We aim higher than our reach.

We may feel it is past our powers, so we exhaust our powers. But only those who go beyond their powers come on powers beyond their own.

Only those who have run as far as they could, get their second wind, and run farther than they could.

What race are you running?

An old man named Socrates, condemned to die, refused to flee his prison when his friends arranged for him to flee —not because he did not want to live. He wanted to live. But he wanted to live as he thought was fit for a man. Death was a swift runner, he said, but so was unrighteousness; and if he had to be overtaken by one or the other, he had rather it would be death.

It is important that you win the victory. It is important that you perfect the art and master the skill and put out the fire and find the hidden treasure and save the life.

But when the crowds that cheered you in the street are gone and you come home to your room alone, what then? In the silence of your own soul, have you the victory? And in your own mind, are you the master there?

Life goes on for a lifetime

A man needs victories, though mainly the victories he needs are small. For a few passing incidents occasionally to turn out well is enough to make most of us feel that life is on our side.

It is not events that determine a man's life—the great events, least of all.

There are so few of these.

How many great thoughts has the greatest thinker had in a lifetime? A half dozen? Hardly so many. Probably no more than one.

How many battles has the greatest conqueror won? A half dozen? Certainly no more. And he may have suffered almost as many defeats.

The greatest poets and composers have written, at most, a dozen great pieces. The greatest scientists have made three or four discoveries. The greatest storytellers have told perhaps a few great stories.

But life goes on for a lifetime.

You live moment by moment every minute of every hour of every day of every week of all the years of your life.

You wake, you rise.

You wash, you take care of your body's needs, you eat.

You work, you seek amusement, you take rest.
You talk, you listen, you go alone.
You sleep.
All the time, you think.
Even when you sleep, you dream.
What are you moment by moment?
What are you on the inside of yourself?
What are you when you are you?
You can fool others.
You can fool yourself.
But you cannot fool life.

You have to be you

The world may take me by my title or my clothes or my car or my bank balance or my speech.

But when no one is mouthing my title; when I have hung up my clothes and parked my car; when the bank is shut for the night; when I am naked in my own room, in the solitariness of myself; when I lie down on my own bed like any other man and hope for sleep, or rise in the morning from my dreams—what am I then?

It does not matter much then whether I am the president or the general or the holy man.

What matters is what I am myself.

I have to be me.

You have to be you.

The things we have—the titles and possessions and pretensions—are like masks and costumes that an actor wears.

But who wears the mask?

The real person is all that counts.

The real person is all that is alive.

Life does not ask you to be true to what you are not, but to what you are.

Life asks no impossibles.

It does not ask the gardener to be the king. It asks him to tend his garden. That is a very great thing.

It does not ask the king to be the holy man. It asks him to tend his kingdom. That, too, is a very great thing.

Am I a sheep?

I had better not put on a lion's skin.

I may encounter a lion hunter. Or a lion. Or even another sheep.

It is a very wonderful thing to be a lion, but it is just as wonderful to be a sheep.

We have our own truth to be true to. If there is a higher truth for us to come to, we will not come to it by being false to what we have come to be now.

2

*

A sparrow's tale

❃

Once a sparrow was tending his nest when he saw a snake climbing up the tree toward him. In a twitter of fright, he rose up into the sky and went to find the eagle.

"He is the king of the birds," said the sparrow, "and he will make short shrift of this rascally snake." After a while he came to where the eagle was. But the eagle, as becomes an eagle, was soaring among the updrafts, much higher than the sparrow could fly. So the sparrow called to him.

"There is a snake climbing up the tree to eat the eggs in my nest," said the sparrow. "You are the king of the birds. Come and chase him away."

But the eagle was having such a wonderful time being an eagle and it was such a beautiful day for soaring that he decided to act kingly and pay no attention to the sparrow.

"You don't get updrafts like this every day," he thought crossly. "Anyway, I'll be down in a minute or two."

So he continued to soar while the sparrow flew around and around in hectic circles far below him.

Meanwhile the snake continued to climb.

Suddenly past the sparrow darted a swallow.

"Good swallow," cried the sparrow, "you are the swiftest

of birds. A snake is climbing the tree to eat my eggs. Will you fly on your swift wings and summon the blue jays and the blackbirds to drive him away?"

"I would be happy to," said the swallow, "some other day. But today is my day to return to Capistrano, where I was going when you stopped me. Crowds of people are waiting. So of course I cannot take time out for anything else."

The swallow flew on.

By this time the snake had reached the nest and had begun to eat the eggs. When the sparrow saw this, he became infuriated. Screaming curses at the top of his voice, he darted at the snake. He set up such a clamor and rush that all the other sparrows in all the trees around came flying up to see what the matter was. When they saw the snake, they, too, began to scream at him and to fly at him with darting beaks and whirling wings, pecking at his head and pecking at his tail, so that the snake, bleeding from a dozen wounds, slithered down the tree as fast as he could and hid in a hole in the ground.

"But he has eaten my eggs," wept the sparrow.

"Why didn't you raise the alarm when you first saw him?" said one of his friends. "We would have driven him off before he reached your nest."

Then the sparrow saw that he did not need the power of the eagle or the swiftness of the swallow; he had only to be a sparrow among sparrows.

A window on infinity

Do not refuse to light your light because you are not a star.

A glowworm may be just as delightful as a star is.

A firefly may be just as much a part of a summer night.

A candle may have just as deep and unforgettable a meaning.

And was a star always a star?

Or was it first a spark somewhere in space, a bit of star-stuff that caught fire and glowed? It glowed as brightly as it could, so that the star-stuff all around it was drawn to it and began to glow, too. So it became the light of a world.

Once I went to a meeting in a huge hall. It was full of people like myself. When I went in, I was given a match. It was only one match and I was only one person.

After I had gotten to my seat, the lights were put out. In the dark a man said, "Light your match."

I lit my match. My one match made a feeble flickering light.

But everyone else in the huge hall had lit his feeble flickering match, too—and the hall was filled, not with a feeble flicker, but with such a deep, warm glow that it still shines in my mind, many years after my little match burnt down to its blackened end and flickered out.

Do you sometimes feel that you are only a very small match?

A match makes a little light. But it is enough to see by, even on the darkest night. It is enough to find your way by and to help another find his way by. The smallest match makes the difference between light and darkness—and that is an infinite difference.

A match is a light—and who can say what a light may be? Even the least light!

Every time we strike a light, we open a window on infinity.

If you are a star, give out your light.

If you are a match, give out your light.

A warm fire in the kitchen stove

Match or star, you are yet more than you think yourself to be.

O little human match, I do not know you, but if I knew you, I would love you.

I have never gotten to know anyone well that I did not love him. It is only those we do not know well that we do not like. The better we get to know them, the more we like them.

Most of the time, the appearance of things obstructs our vision. We see the human form and touch the human mind. We accept the customary and call it commonplace.

But people are not what they seem to be. They are not what they look like, not what they act like. We cannot tell what they are like by looking at their masks and medals, their costumes and pretensions. They are not what we see them to be. They are not what they see themselves to be.

People are much like the houses they live in. You cannot be sure from what the outside looks like as to what the inside is like to live in. The outside may be beautiful or ugly, inviting or austere, but the inside may not be like that at all. You have to live in a house to come to be at home in it.

People live on the inside of themselves. When you get to know them from the inside out instead of from the outside in, you find that they keep a warm fire on the kitchen stove—even in a castle with donjons and battlements.

When you get past the outward differences down toward the inward heart, you find that they are very much like you.

Do you wonder what am I like? What are you like? I am very much like you. When we get past the obvious differences, this is.

Are you nothing more than what you obviously are? Is there not something in you that is more than your human thoughts and human form? Are you not more than your shortcomings and attainments? What in you measures shortcomings and attainments?

Do you not feel that you are more than I am aware of, more than you are aware of, more than you have ever been?

When we look with eyes of love

There is so much more to all of us than the obvious.

A few times in my life I have gotten a glimpse of the real self of a person. It was only for an anguished moment and only because I looked with eyes of love.

But for an anguished moment I looked with eyes of love and I saw. I cannot say what I saw, but I knew that it was something inexpressibly beautiful. I shall always believe I was looking at being as it really is, and I saw beauty naked.

I believe that is what I would see if I saw the real self of you. But I have to look with eyes of love.

That is why lovers go around starry-eyed. They have seen through what is form to what is real, and it has left them dazzled. They can only murmur, "Beautiful."

We look at what they are looking at and wonder how they can see so much in such a plain creature. But it is our vision that is imperfect.

Love raises vision to a higher power that eye charts cannot measure.

People are like poems

People are like great works of art. Fall in love with them and you may see clear through to reality.

Have you ever had a great work of art—a poem or a piece of music or a painting—open its soul and reveal itself to you?

Great works of art have a kind of hidden luminosity about them. A poem, for instance, is just some lines, on a page in a book. But once in a while, if you fall in love with it, a poem reveals itself to you. The lines glow, and suddenly you see through the words into life. You see truth as if it were a clear shining.

People are like that. They, too, glow with a kind of hidden luminosity when you get past the obvious.

When I see through what you are not

Always, when I see through what you are not to what you are, the closer I come to the real you—the person you really are—the more I am aware that you are someone original, unique, extraordinary.

There is nothing and nobody else like you. You are necessary to infinity; it would be less than infinite without you. Whatever you are, life needs you to be complete.

What are you?

It is as much to be a child as to be a man.

It is as important to be a gardener as to be a king.

The orchestra is not complete without a piccolo player; the symphony waits on his gay note as much as on the one who plays the tuba.

Second violinists, a great conductor once said, are even harder to find than first violinists.

Be what you are.

There is no virtue in being a banker.

There is no virtue in being a beggar.

Virtue consists in being what you are.

It is not by being false to what you are, but by being true to what you are, that you grow to be more than you are.

To watch a water bug

I have a lily pond in my back yard.

Often on a morning of late summer, I sit there and watch a water bug.

It is an ugly bug, about an inch and a half long, thick, muddy-colored, awkward, and slow-moving. A cumbersome crawler from the bottom of the pond, it has lived its life burrowing in the mud.

But now, on this day, it crawls out of the mud, out of the water, out into the air, where it has never been before. It climbs through this strange element and fastens itself upon a rock. Hours pass. It becomes stiff, hard, dry. I have often wondered if it dies—to itself, at least. Certainly, the water bug is no more.

After a while it becomes so dry and brittle that it splits open, and out of the shell of its former self steps something more than a water bug.

Its bedraggled wings are hardly wings, at first, but slowly they stretch wide on either side, long, tapering, transparent, glistening; the mud-crawler lengthens into a green-gold air-shaped thing; then on a sudden breeze the wings flash and cast themselves upon the air—and the water bug is a dragonfly!

If we did not know it to be true, who would believe it when we pointed to the ugly water bug and said that it is the most graceful of all things that fly.

You have your own truth, like no one else's.

Be true to it.

Truth is always a thing that flies.

Who shall say where its wings will carry you?

3

*

This is the very life!

*

Once there was a woodchopper.

He was a good woodchopper and a devout man. He exaggerated only a little about the grade of wood he sold and hardly at all as to its measure. A tithe of all he made he gave to Sylvanus, who was the god of wood lots and woodchoppers.

Every evening he prayed to Sylvanus before he fell asleep. Every morning on his way to work in the wood he would pause at a little shrine by the road. There he would leave an offering, if only a few flowers or a few pennies, and he would say a prayer.

The god was much touched by this unusual devotion, and one morning seeing him at his prayers, decreed that henceforth whatever the woodchopper wished would be granted.

That morning when he left the shrine, the woodchopper did not go to his usual place to work. Instead he climbed high up the east side of the mountain on the west side of the kingdom to a grove where very tall and very old pine trees were growing. The woodchopper had heard that the grove was sacred to Sylvanus, and he had always refrained from cutting trees in it. But this morning he felt impelled to go there.

He had promised his cousin, who was a storekeeper in the city, to bring him a load of wood. So he walked among the trees looking for one that he might cut into logs. Most of the trees in the grove were giants, some of them towering two hundred feet above his head. The woodchopper, dwarfed and humbled by them, felt that he did not dare touch such a tree as one of these.

There were many saplings, but these were too small to be worth cutting. So he walked along, looking at the trees and mainly thinking about life. As he did, his thoughts turned to his cousin, for whom he was chopping the wood.

How pleasant it would be to wake up like his cousin in a soft bed in a warm house and sell beautiful objects all day long in a lighted store to interesting people who would be coming in to buy, and not have to go out as he was doing, into the damp woods on a frosty morning and chop down trees, which was very hard work!

Just then he saw a tree. It was about fifty feet high and a little twisted at the top.

"Just what I've been looking for," he said to himself. "Sylvanus will never mind my taking this one, even if it is his grove."

He took his ax out of the pack on his back and brought it whistling down against the tree trunk. As he grunted with the effort, he could not help again thinking of how hard his life was compared to the effortless life of his cousin.

"How I wish I could change with him," he said to himself.

After he had delivered the wood, he walked through his cousin's store. He looked with envy at all the beautiful and strange objects that glittered on the crowded shelves, smiled at all the customers who came in, and listened with delight to the hum and clatter of life that rose from the streets outside every time the door opened.

At last he said to his cousin, "What a lucky man you are! I wish I had a fine store like this!"

"How lucky we both are then!" said his cousin. "For I'm anxious to sell it to you. Just this morning my wife and I decided to retire. We would like to live in the country. You have a fine wood lot and a rustic cabin that we could make cozy. We would take that as a down payment and arrange a loan for you at the bank that you can pay off in easy terms from the profits of the store."

The words had hardly been spoken before the deal was completed. The woodchopper had borrowed the money he needed to borrow, signed the papers he needed to sign, taken charge of his store, and moved into the second-floor apartment over it. There he was, a storekeeper and a city dweller, with hot and cold running water, central plumbing, central heating, and a mortgage.

"Ah, this is the very life!" he felt.

And so it was.

He settled down to keeping his store and enjoying the many sights and amusements that the city provided. He was a cheerful, amiable fellow. He made friends, worked hard, learned quickly, and he prospered.

But one day he received notice that the payment on the mortgage was due.

When he looked into the matter, he found, to his amazement, that this payment took almost all the money he had made and left him little to show for all his work.

This grieved him, but off he went to make his payment to the banker.

The banker's office was a sumptuous one, all leather and

mahogany, with a fine picture on the wall, a silver carafe on his desk, and a beautiful girl to usher visitors in and out.

"A banker's life must be a pleasant one!" said the woodchopper-storekeeper. "How I wish I were a banker!"

The banker cleared his throat importantly and poured himself a drink from his silver carafe. "Ah, but there are many worries and responsibilities," he said, smiling a superior smile. "To be a banker requires a college education, years of graduate study in an accredited school of finance, and many more years of business experience."

On the way home the woodchopper-storekeeper happened to pass a street peddler who was selling lottery tickets.

"Buy a ticket, mister, and win a fortune," said the peddler.

"Go away," said the storekeeper.

But the peddler did not go away. He came sidling after him, thrusting the dirty lottery ticket into his face and getting underfoot till the storekeeper had to stop to keep from falling over him.

He was a disreputable-looking little fellow with a puckered face and shifty eyes. His clothes were dirty green rags, made of a strange fabric the storekeeper had never seen before. He would have sworn it was woven out of pine needles except that he knew that was impossible.

"Buy a ticket," said the peddler, "and the gods will smile on you." He smiled.

"I don't have any money," said the storekeeper.

"You've enough to buy a lottery ticket," said the peddler.

"But I don't," said the storekeeper. "Look." And he turned out his pockets to show how empty they were.

But they were not empty. Out of one fluttered a bill.

"Just the right amount!" cried the peddler. He caught it in mid-air, stuffed the ticket into the hand of the storekeeper, and disappeared around the corner.

The storekeeper laughed.

"I thought I had nothing left, so I might as well have nothing left." He put the lottery ticket in his pocket and forgot all about it until a newspaper reporter called him on the telephone. He had just won the grand prize.

"This beats keeping store," he said to himself. "I was lucky once. Who knows? I may be lucky again. Anyway, I'll try." So he began to invest in the stock market.

Every morning, after his prayers to Sylvanus, he took twelve silver pins and shutting his eyes stuck them into lists of the names of stocks. These he bought or sold, depending on whether the pin had gone into the first part or the last part of the name.

Whenever he bought a stock, it immediately went up. Whenever he sold a stock, it immediately went down.

In a short time he had amassed a fortune.

"I believe now I have enough education in matters of finance to try my luck at being a banker," he thought.

So he opened a bank.

He showed the same remarkable ability as a banker that he had in the lottery and the stock market. In a short time he had bankrupted most of the other banks in the city, bought them up at a low price, and become the country's principal money vendor.

He had an office all leather and mahogany, with an antique Persian carpet on the floor. He had not only a silver carafe on his desk; hidden behind a wall that opened when he pressed a button, he had an entire kitchen. He had expensive paintings on his walls. He did not understand any of the paintings, but the art dealers assured him they were great art, and for his own pleasure he kept on his desk a simple drawing a friend had made of the little cabin on the mountain where he had lived when he was a woodchopper. He had two beautiful girls to usher visitors in and out.

On the most exclusive boulevard in the city he had a comfortable old four-story house full of uncomfortable modern furniture. He had a chauffeur to drive him back and forth in his two limousines. He had a limousine to make business calls in and a limousine to make social calls in.

"This is the very life," thought the woodchopper-storekeeper-banker.

And so it was.

He lived it to the full until one day his two beautiful girls who ushered visitors in and out of his office ushered in four visitors.

These were ordinary-looking men wearing felt hats and carrying brief cases.

The first man handed him his card. "I am from the Internal Revenue Service," he said. "You have made so much money that you owe us ninety per cent of all you have made."

The second man handed him his card. "I am from the State Tax Bureau," he said. "You can be glad I'm not piggish like these federal fellows, who in fairness ought to split with us. You owe us only five per cent."

The third man handed him his card. "I am the county collector. You owe us three per cent," he said.

"I am the city collector. You only owe us one and a half per cent," said the fourth man, almost apologetically.

The banker added up all these figures on a piece of paper. "That comes to ninety-nine and a half per cent for you," he said.

They nodded.

"And one half of one per cent for me," he said.

They nodded.

"You realize it may take me a little time to get your share of my money for you," he said.

"I'll give you one day," said the first man, rising and smiling.

"Two days," said the second man, amiably.

"Three days," said the third man, affably.

"Four days," said the fourth man, benevolently.

The banker thanked them all and showed them to the door. When he came back, he sat at his desk thinking.

"I thought it would be wonderful to be a banker," he said. "But I can see that the only man in this country who has a life worth living is the king. He lives on the money the rest of us make. If I were king, then I could really live—and do things for the country, too. How I wish I were king!"

He looked up from his desk to see that one of his beautiful girls had ushered in another visitor.

This was a strange-looking man. He had a shaved head, a puckered face, and squinty eyes. He had on a green robe. If the banker had not known such a thing was impossible, he would have sworn that the fabric was woven out of pine needles.

"Who are you?" asked the banker.

"I am the high priest of Sylvanus," said the man in the green robe. "I believe you made an arrangement with my master to give him the tenth part of all you made. He sent me to collect."

"The gods, too!" thought the woodchopper, but he kept his thoughts to himself while he peered shrewdly at his visitor and weighed the matter.

Then, because he was an honorable man; even more, because he was a little afraid of Sylvanus; above all, because the tax collectors were going to get his money anyway—he wrote out a check. He chuckled as he wrote it out, for he made it, not for one tenth, but for three tenths of all he had made, which was the maximum amount the law permitted him to give.

He told the priest to cash the check at once.

The priest gave him his blessing.

Then he said:

"This money is exactly the sum we need to make our operation a complete success. It will buy off the three people we have needed to buy off—the chief of police, the king's mistress, and the high priest of the god of cities, Urbanus.

"As you undoubtedly agree, our lord Sylvanus has never had the honor we feel he should have in this kingdom. Country folk love him, but city people have never paid him much heed.

"So we who are his followers have decided to make him chief god.

"To achieve this, we have formed an organization. Its members are all those who feel they have never had the honors they should have. As you may guess, this makes quite a large group. It is headed by two admirals who never got to be chief admiral and three generals and a colonel in the Air Force who never got to be chief general. Then there are several cabinet members who never got to be prime minister.

"Tonight we are going to stage a coup. After the coup, we will need a new king. Do not be surprised if the election lights on you."

That night the coup took place. It was a bloodless one; only a few hundred people were killed. The old king was spirited off his throne and out of the country; unfortunately on the way the car in which he was riding ran off a cliff into the sea and the king and every member of the royal family drowned.

The prime minister and a few other stubborn opponents of progress were thrown into dungeons or fled the country. The chief admiral and chief general were generously retired on admirable pensions. To their posts and to all the other posts in the country, members of the revolutionary junta were appointed.

Sylvanus was declared to be the chief god. His high priest became the first priest of the kingdom. He immediately appeared on all the TV networks and announced that, the old king being dead, it was his duty to find a new king. This, with appropriate ceremonies and incantations that took up all the prime time for three nights and three days, he proceeded to do.

"There are certain signs," said he, "that we must pay attention to.

"First, we need a man of business acumen, so that he can give the country efficient government.

"Second, we need a man who is a devout worshiper of the gods, so that the gods will favor us.

"Third, we need a man of humble origin, so that he will represent the people."

All these signs pointed so clearly to the woodchopper-storekeeper-banker that in a day of almost universal jubilation, he was crowned king. The high priest crowned him in the name of Sylvanus and anointed him with pine-tree oil.

"This is the very life," he thought as he mounted on his throne.

And so it was.

He had five palaces, one in the middle of the kingdom, one by the sea, one by the mountain, one by the lake, and one by the desert. The smallest had a hundred rooms. He had twelve limousines and a foreign sports car. He had a chauffeur and a footman for each limousine. He had a motorcycle escort to clear the streets when he drove the sports car. He had a royal guard to march up and down in front of his palaces and have their picture taken by tourists. He had secret-service men to keep autograph seekers, assassins, and other strangers from sneaking in the back doors. He had bevies of beautiful girls to do anything he wanted. He not only had lovely op-art, pop-art, and slop-art paintings; he had only to turn to his councilor of arts and say, "Don't you think these paintings on the walls are getting almost understandable?" The councilor would run to the telephone, call up an artist, and the artist would immediately begin to paint a newer and more incomprehensible painting.

He had nothing to do but think up ways to spend the money the rest of the country made. He was very, very happy.

But he had been king only a short while when he became ill. At first his sickness seemed no more than a stomachache caused by his excessively happy way of life; but under the care of his doctors, he became rapidly worse and worse.

Each doctor treated him for something different. They could not agree on their diagnosis as to what was wrong. Most of them said it was a virus he had picked up in the woods, where he still liked to walk, but as to which virus they were not sure. He himself said that it had started as an allergic reaction to the oil the high priest had poured on his head.

But whatever it was, at last it became apparent to everyone—even to the king—that the malady was mortal.

The king called all his doctors and wise men and councilors and courtiers to his bedside.

"I thought it would be wonderful to be a king," he said. "But what good is it to be king if you aren't going to live!"

The courtiers did not answer this, but they all thought the king had made a point.

"Long life!" said the king. "Do you who are going to go on living when I am dead realize how valuable long life is? I never did. Now I think of all the people and things in my kingdom that will live much longer than I. How unfair that I, the king, should die and all of you should live!"

The courtiers said nothing, but it was obvious from their expressions that they had no thought personally of trying to reverse the situation.

The king continued to muse. "I wonder what is the longest-lived of all things? Do you know, my courtiers? Whatever it is, that is the most fortunate of all things! How I wish I were that!"

Still the courtiers said nothing. They did not know what is the longest-lived of all things, and they did not see how knowing it would do them any good.

After a while he sent them away.

When the doctors and wise men and councilors and courtiers had left, one little man remained behind. Now he drew near the bedside of the king.

"O king," he said, "I heard you ask what is the longest-lived thing in your kingdom. It happens that I have made a study of such matters. The longest lived things in your kingdom are a species of pine trees that grow in a grove on the east side of the mountain on the west side of your kingdom."

"How long do these trees live?" asked the king.

"They live three thousands years," said the man.

"Three thousand years!" cried the king. "And here I am

dying at fifty-five. Oh, how I wish I could change places with those trees."

"Your majesty," said the little man, "I have made a profound study of those trees, and I know the secret of their long life."

The king looked at the man. He was not much to look at, a skinny little man with a puckered face and eyes that looked in different directions. He had a beard, a wart on his nose, and needed a haircut. He wore an old green suit, shiny in the seat and baggy at the knees. It looked as if it were woven out of pine needles, except that the king knew this was impossible.

"Who are you?" asked the king.

"My name is Dr. Da Silva. I am one of your majesty's physicians," said the man. "It happens that I have extracted from the sap of these trees a very potent drug. Whoever takes it lives as long as a tree."

"You have a drug that will make it possible for me to live three thousand years?" said the king.

"Yes, your majesty."

"Then give it to me. Give it to me at once."

"Alas, I hesitate to do that," said the little man. "Like many modern drugs, it has not been thoroughly tested. It may have disagreeable and unforeseen side effects."

"Pish for side effects! You say this drug will enable me to live three thousand years?"

"There is no question," said the little man, "that the drug will enable you to live as long as a pine tree. But when you take the drug, everything has to be just right. There is only one place where the drug can do its most efficacious work. For me to give you the drug, you will have to come with me to the grove where the pine trees grow on the east side of the mountain on the west side of your kingdom."

"If I will live as long as those pine trees, let us go at once," said the king. He let the little man help him out of bed and into a royal robe—he did not wait to put on his crown. The two of them went down the long staircase to the royal garage, slipped into one of the royal limousines, and chugged off into the country till they reached the mountain on the west side of the kingdom. Here, puffing and panting, they climbed the slope to the grove where the pine trees grew that lived for three thousand years.

After they had rested a few minutes and could breathe again, the little man opened his doctor's satchel, which was made of the same strange green stuff as his clothes. He took out some odd-shaped tools and quickly drew from one of the tallest pine trees a thick, dark, seething fluid. This he mixed with a brown, sticky liquid in a curious container shaped like a pine cone. From a small vial he poured a stream of glittering green powder into this mixture, which immediately bubbled up and exploded with a flash, giving off a peculiar odor, like caves and sunlight and wet pine woods. But in a few moments the odor dissipated and the foaming flames went out.

This was the drug.

It was a green, oily, smoking liquid. The little man handed the pine-cone cup that held it to the king.

The king tasted it.

"Not bad," he said. "A little like the turpentine and molasses my mother used to make me drink when I was a boy. Do I drink it all?"

"To the last drop," said the little man.

The king drank.

Instantly a shudder that seemed to start at the very core of his being ran through him. His heart exploded as if it were ten thousand fireworks. He felt a green flame running in his veins. Every cell of his body swelled with a tremendous surge of life. The feeling of change was so intense that he felt heady and thought he might faint, but he did not fall.

He had a sense of standing on extreme tiptoe, yet he felt stronger, steadier, sturdier than he ever had. He had never stood so straight. He had never felt so tall.

"I feel completely made over," the king called out to the little man. "You have saved my life."

Somehow the little man seemed even littler than he had before. The king seemed to tower above him. He looked down.

"But the drug is causing a few hallucinations," he said. For he had an impression of his limbs being covered by rough bark instead of by his kingly robes.

He tried to lift his foot. But he had a sense of being rooted to the ground.

He started to bring his hands up in front of his face. But now he could not move them, and when he caught a glimpse of them out of the corner of his eye, he could see that his arms had grown much longer and they, too, were covered with rough bark. His fingers had all grown longer, too, and from their ends needles were sprouting.

He looked again at the little man.

Now the little man was far beneath him—forty feet at least!—and his face held a half-fascinated, half-horrified expression, as if he were not sure whether he had failed or succeeded.

"I'm turning into a pine tree," cried the king.

"I-I told you there might be some disagreeable side effects," said the little man. Suddenly he disappeared down the mountain side.

When the king was left alone, his metamorphosis completed itself quickly. In a matter of minutes, he was altogether a pine tree. He judged he was a tree about fifty feet high, much smaller than the great two-hundred-foot-high trees around him.

"Is there anybody here who can hear me?" he said, not expecting an answer, not even sure he had a voice. His voice came as a soft rustling of needles.

"Hear you!" said one of the tallest trees. "You've been making such a disgraceful commotion, who could help but hear you!"

"But I'm a pine tree!"

"Of course you're a pine tree. What else would you imagine yourself to be!"

"Nothing," said the king quickly. He thought he had better. "But I haven't been a pine tree very long, and I'm not used to it yet."

"True," said the other, nodding its head in the breeze, "you've only been a pine tree—hmmm!—fifty-five years, as I remember. When you've been around two thousand seven hundred and thirty-six years like me, you really know what it is to be a pine tree!"

"You are two thousand seven hundred thirty-six years old!"

"Oh, give or take a few years. That's what it was the last time I counted my rings—though that doesn't give a sure count, the experts say. But you know something, young sapling? I still feel as young and hearty as I did at fifty-five!"

The woodchopper-storekeeper-banker-king-pine tree considered his plight, and the longer he considered it the less it seemed like a plight.

If he was fifty-five years old and he was going to live till he was three thousand years old, that meant he had at least twenty-nine hundred and forty-five years still to live.

He felt all resentment fading away. He settled back against the mountain side, let down his roots in the moist, dark earth, stretched out his branches to the cool, clean air. The wind touched him, and he felt what it is like to dance in the wind. The sunlight touched him, and he felt what it is like to live in the sun.

Two birds flew by, lit on a bough, and spoke to him pleasantly. A squirrel that ran up his trunk proved to be a friendly gossip. The squirrel knew everything about everybody on the mountain.

The pine tree began to enjoy being a pine tree.

"This is the very life," it said.

And so it was.

Just then a man came climbing up the mountain. The man walked from tree to tree, looking up at them all.

"Too big," he would say as he looked at one. "Too small," he would say as he looked at another. So he went until at last he reached the pine tree that had been the king.

"Just what I've been looking for," he said. "Sylvanus will never mind my taking this one, even if it is his grove." Without another word, he drew from his pack a glistening ax and drove its sharp blade deep into the tree trunk.

The tree let out a howl of anguish. "Oh, if I could only be a woodchopper again! I can see that is the happiest fate in the world."

It had no sooner uttered the words than woodchopper it was. It was not a tree but the man with the ax poised over his head about to bring it down once more on the tree trunk.

As the woodchopper realized where he was, he stopped and let the ax slip slowly to the ground. He shook his head as if to clear it.

"I must have been having a horrible daydream!" he said at last.

Then he shivered all over as if he had caught a chill. He felt so peculiar that he sat down on a stump. What was wrong he was not sure, but after a few minutes he decided that whatever it was, he had no more heart for woodchopping that day. He would get his cousin's wood another time.

He put his ax away and went back down the mountain to his hut.

When he got to his hut, he shut the door and built a roaring blaze in his fireplace. He poured himself a glass of red wine. He broke off a piece of black pumpernickel bread and a little strong cheese. He ate and he drank. Then he sat in front of his fire until late into the night, thinking many strange thoughts.

At last he rose and went to bed, but first he made his usual prayer to his favorite god, Sylvanus.

"Dear god of this world of woods and woodchoppers," he said, "thank you for all my blessings."

He pulled the warm covers up over his head, and as he fell asleep, he thought, "Ah, this is the very life!"

And is this not so?

Trumpets are for triumph

You are meant for greatness, but in what does your greatness consist? Surely it consists in being what you are, not in being what you are not.

What you are—this is enough.

We cannot weigh a morning-glory in the same scale in which we weigh an oak.

How do we weigh a morning-glory?

Where once I grew them in my garden as flowers, now they spring up as weeds.

When they were flowers, they were a pampered flower. Their seeds had to be coaxed to germinate; their roots had to be coaxed to take hold; their vines had to be coaxed to grow. Slowly, leisurely, but luxuriously, they spread all summer long, covering a wall at last with the blue bounty of their bloom.

Now that they are weeds, I search them out to uproot them. Yet they push up, shy and small, among the rocks and at the edge of things.

It has been five years since I have grown them as flowers. Yet in spite of my perennial efforts—not too methodical, I admit—they still survive.

On a day in late summer or early fall, I go out and there—

a few inches of twisted stems scarcely lifting above the ground their handful of worm-gnawed leaves—there a morning-glory is tilting toward the sun its valiant trumpet.

I know nothing so fragile as a morning-glory, crumpled by the chance wing of any passing insect, lasting an hour, two hours, half a day at most.

This is a ragged flimsy of a flower, a swirl of paper petals —no, not so tough as paper. The heat of the sun is enough to fade it; the brush of the wind is enough to tear it; a morning is enough to wither it.

Yet there it is, life itself, the very essence and spirit of life. In spite of time and me and all its other enemies, it lifts its tattered trumpet high and blows its song of life.

Trumpets are for triumph.

Blow your life-colored trumpets, morning-glories! Blow to the shapeless clay and the earless stones.

I catch a kind of morning-glory courage from you. I see, not how uncertain life is, but how persistent life is; not how weak life is, but how strong life is—the least life there is, is mightier than all the non-life that may be. And I sense that I—no less than you—am part of something easy to uproot but very hard to kill.

Of victory and defeat

Have you won great victories? You have the glory of them.

Have you borne great defeats? You have the glory of these, too.

Have you ever wondered whether it will be by your victories or your defeats that life will measure you?

It is not Wellington who comes to mind when we think of Waterloo. It is Napoleon, who lost the battle.

If we remember Gettysburg, it is Pickett we remember, leading his long gray line of men on their immortal charge, not to victory, but to disaster.

There are many beautiful Arches of Triumph, but the most beautiful building any man ever built is the Taj Mahal, a tomb a king built for the woman he loved.

The trumpets blow not only for the victors, but for those who fell.

Men bear the hero home on their shoulders—whether he is waving to the cheering crowds, or he is lying still while they weep as he is borne by.

Did he bear life forward?

You who bear him on your shoulders bear life forward, too.

The stone the builders rejected

Life does not demand, "Did you always do what you set out to do?"

No one has ever done all he set out to do. No matter what we did, we thought we might do more. We might have run faster, thought higher, built the building more foursquare.

Did you hit the bull's-eye every time you fired? Why did you aim at such an easy target—and do you dare try one shot more?

Sometimes it is the distance we fell short that is the measure of our height.

We have all been given the same clay to work with. Some of us have been given a little more agile fingers, some a little more clay.

But it has never been those with the most clay who have made the most of it. Sometimes it has been those with the least clay; they had to stretch their minds.

Nor is it those with the most agile fingers. Sometimes it has been those with the least agile fingers. Sometimes it has only been after we have lost our fingers that we got down in earnest to what we had to do.

It is often the weakest lad who becomes the strongest man.

The stone the builders rejected has become the chief cornerstone.

If we waited to make music

If we waited until we were perfect musicians before we played an instrument, there would be no music in the world.

It is only because we fumble at one-finger pieces that someday chords like thunder roll out from under our hands. And our one-fingered fumbling fills our hearts with music as much as will our mighty harmonies when we have become the master.

Life does not use only the good people to do good, or the brave to win battles, or the wise to find the light.

What brave deeds have been done by frightened persons! How much selflessness has been shown by selfish men! What great truths have been discovered by those who had little learning!

You do not need to be perfect to help me to find my perfection. You do not need to be good to help me to be better. You do not need to be strong to help me to stand.

If only those who were professors taught us, how little we would learn.

A handful of earth

Do you think you are not much?

A handful of earth is not much. Yet if we knew how to draw forth the power contained in it, we could reshape the globe and everything on it.

If there is so much power in a handful of earth, how much power is in you, who are much more than a handful of earth.

If you could draw forth the power contained in you, you would change the history of the human race.

You may not be much, but you are enough.

One man is enough to change the world.

One man has changed the world many times—one man with a single thought, one man with a little faith, one man with a sense of something needing to be done that was his to do.

One man! You are one.

You probably had a better start in life than George Washington Carver, who was born a Negro slave. You probably had more education than Mahomet or Joan of Arc, who were illiterate, or Edison, whose teacher sent him home from school because he was a dunce, or even Shakespeare, who went through grammar school. You probably had better health than Epictetus, who was a cripple, or Homer, who was blind, or Beethoven, who was deaf when he wrote some of his best music, or Dostoevski, who was an epileptic.

You are probably younger than Grandma Moses, who was seventy-eight when she started to paint, and older than John Keats, who was dead when he was twenty-five.

Most of the things worth doing have been done by men and women who had no particular qualification for doing them.

They were just men and women who refused to settle for the obvious limitations.

Who placed on you the limitations you have settled for?

Who holds you back now?

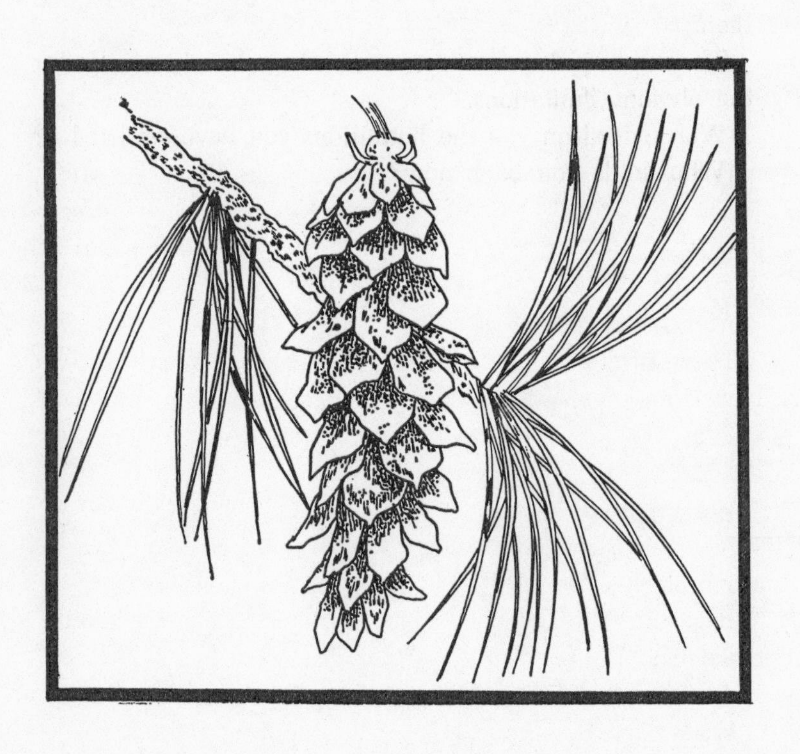

Victory has broken wings

In the Louvre in Paris is the statue of the Venus de Milo. When we think of the perfection of beauty, this statue—among all the works of men—is most likely to come into our mind.

And this is strange. Because it has no arms.

There is yet another statue in the Louvre. When visitors have been asked which one of all the objects in the museum has moved them most, more of them have mentioned this statue than any other.

We call it the Winged Victory.

And this is strange. Because it has no head and its wings are broken.

It is strange that such a shattered block of marble should make us think of victory; yet it does.

A victory with broken wings!

What does it say to us to have such power to move us?

In this disfigured but triumphant image do we see our own humanity?

Do we see man the undaunted—not because he is without fear, but because he keeps coming forward even through his fears?

Do we see man the undefeatable—not because he is not

defeated, but because he keeps coming forward even through his defeats?

Do we see man the immortal—not because he does not die, but because he has a spirit mightier than death?

Do we see man's spirit, battered but not destroyed, unfinished but emerging, broken-winged but rising!

Life has many exquisite small perfections. We sip them and enjoy our moment of delight. But soon we turn away. However sweet, however beautiful, they cannot content us.

For we sense that at the core of things, there is something more—something with broken wings, but more. We cannot see it whole; we can only reach for it and have faith that it is there. We disfigure it in embodiment—not because it is less than perfect, but because it is beyond our power to perfect.

This is the height too high for our attaining—but we climbed until our strength gave out.

This is the country too vast for us to take—but we found it.

This is the perfection too complete for our perfecting—but we caught its spirit.

Perfection is not always the flawless and complete, but may be the disfigured and unfinished.

Victory may have broken wings.

But on its broken wings we rise.

Not a monument, but an encampment

A man wants to be more than he is—even more than man.

He is never content for long with any goal he reaches. He has to aim higher than he can reach.

Life is not for attaining, but for striving.

It is not the end of the tale that makes it worth the telling; a great story is great, however it happens to end. The end is only one incident.

If life is moving toward some absolute and ultimate perfection, that is good—but it is not what gives life meaning.

Life finds its meaning here and now, or it will never have meaning. To be alive—to reach and strive and do and become and be—this is all the meaning life needs.

We suffer because we do not reach our own highest expectations, and this is right. But how sad it would be if we did reach them! It would only mean we had held ourselves and life cheap. The ancients said that when the gods do not like someone, they give him all he asks for.

What is victory? What is defeat?

A scientist spends his life in a laboratory, isolating an enzyme—and then never isolates it.

An archaeologist spends his life in a desert, excavating a lost city—and then never gets it uncovered.

A philosopher spends his life in thought, formulating the truth on which all other truths stand for support—and then never gets it written down.

A poet spends his life writing a great poem—and then never perfects it.

The cities of man are the symbols of man's life. Have you gotten the new street paved? We must tear it up again to put in new water mains or make it twice as wide. Have you raised the tower a hundred stories high? The wrecking crew is already on the way—the site is needed for a rocket port.

Life is always building, never built. Life is coming to be, not having been.

Life is not a monument. Life is an encampment. Come tomorrow to the city, and you may find it a wilderness. But come to the wilderness, and you may find a city towering higher than your dreams.

4

*

The golden apples of all men's desire

❋

Once there were two brothers who owned an apple orchard. The land was no better than you might expect it to be. The trees were no better than you might expect them to be. The weather was hardly ever as good as you might expect it to be. But the two brothers worked hard, and the trees usually bore a better crop of apples than they might be expected to bear. So the brothers prospered.

One morning as they sat at breakfast, the elder brother said: "Last night I had an extraordinary dream. I dreamed of an apple tree. It was not like any other apple tree I have ever seen. Everything about it was perfect. No bugs gnawed its leaves. No blemishes marred its fruit. Its apples were the most beautiful apples in the world.

"I tried to pick one. But every time I reached for one, the apple I was reaching for was always beyond my reach, and I heard a voice saying, 'These are the golden apples of all men's desire.'

"At last I woke. Since then I have thought of nothing but that tree and its golden apples."

"That is strange," said his younger brother. "Because I, too, had a dream much like yours. I dreamed of an apple tree. I tried to pick an apple from it. Every time I reached for one, it seemed to melt away into another form, and I heard a voice saying, 'These are the golden apples of all men's desire.'

"But it seemed to me that my tree was in our own orchard, and the apples growing on it did not seem any different from the apples we grow."

"Then our dreams are certainly not the same," said the other. "My apples were not like these." He plucked an apple out of the bowl on the table and held it up. "Look at it. Small, speckled, lopsided. I wouldn't be surprised if it had a worm in it." He broke it open. A worm poked out its head, looked at the two brothers, and drew itself down into its hole again. The older brother laughed. "These may be the golden apples of your desire, but they're not mine. I'd give our whole orchard for a single one of the apples I saw in my dream."

After that things were no longer the same as they had been before.

The older brother worked less and less in the orchard. In the morning he dawdled. In the afternoon he disappeared. When he was in the orchard, his brother was likely to come on him gazing out across the hills instead of pruning or tilling or spraying. "I'm sorry," the older brother would say, "but if you had seen the golden apples of my dream, you wouldn't have much interest in apples that are hardly more than dried prunes."

The younger brother would smile and put his arm around him and then would try to do twice as much work as he had done before, because the work had to be done. He felt that his brother's obsession with his dream would pass. But it did not pass.

One morning the older brother said, "I've decided we ought to sell this orchard. I can work in it no longer. The apples just aren't good enough for me to give my life to. Somewhere there must be the tree of my dream. I'm going to look for it. If a man can't grow perfect apples, why grow any? And if a man doesn't follow his dream, what's a life for?"

The younger brother started to reason with him, but he quickly saw that his brother had made up his mind.

"If this is how you want it," he said, "let me buy your half of our orchard. I have saved a little money, and I can borrow the rest at the bank. You go look for your golden apple tree, and if you find it, you can send me an apple."

It was not hard for the brothers to make a deal. Before the week was out, the younger brother had borrowed the money, bought the orchard, driven his brother to the bus, and waved sadly as he watched the bus vanish down the dusty street.

That afternoon, when he went alone into the orchard, it seemed empty without his brother there. But he loved the orchard, its trees and its apples, though he had to admit they hardly looked like the apples of all men's desire.

The birds were eating some, worms were eating others, and some had already fallen and lay slowly rotting on the damp ground.

But with his brother gone, he had twice as much work to do and he had no time to waste in dreaming. Also, with a mortgage to pay off at the bank, he had no apples to waste by spoiling.

That first afternoon he decided he would make cider out of those falling apples. His grandfather's old cider mill was rusting in a little shed behind the barn. It meant extra work, but it meant extra money; so cider making it would be.

In no time at all he had those apples off the ground, into the cider press, and out of the cider press into a barrel—apples no longer but a clear, sweet stream of golden liquid. The next time he went to town, he poured some into jugs and took it to the store to sell.

"I doubt if I can use it," said the storekeeper. "But there's a new produce man from the city coming in this afternoon. Why don't you talk to him?"

The brother met the produce buyer from the city.

"I don't think I'd be interested," said the produce man. "I represent a grocery firm that handles only fancy groceries."

"Then my cider is exactly what your firm is looking for," said the brother. "This cider is made from a special apple that grows nowhere but in my orchard. My grandfather developed it. He taught us how to make this cider."

He poured some out of his jug. The produce buyer took a long swig. Then he took another long swig.

"This cider is made from the golden apples of all men's desire," said the young man.

"Golden apples of all men's desire, huh?" said the other, draining his glass and holding it out to be filled again. "Never heard of them. But I like it. It *is* different. It tastes like—uh—it tastes like nothing I ever drank before. It's just —uh—different. Tell you what. We'll get our advertising people to write some copy on how your grandfather found the perfect apple for cider. We'll call it Old Granddad's Golden Cider or something like that. I'll take a thousand gallons, and we'll see what we can do."

"I may not have the golden apple of all men's desire," thought the young man as he drove home, "but I do have golden cider made out of my apples. That's almost as good."

And the cider was good. At least, the produce man thought so. He sold the thousand gallons, and he said, "Next year I want ten thousand gallons—and I wouldn't be surprised if we can sell more than that."

The young man borrowed more money, bought more farmland, and planted more apple trees.

"If people like my cider, they'll like my apple butter," he said.

He did not have any apple butter, but he had his grandmother's recipe for it.

He built a building back of his house, bought the best kitchen equipment he could afford, and hired the farm wife who was said to be the best cook in the county. In no time his Grandma's Golden Apple Butter was selling as well as his cider was.

If his apple butter was good, would not his applesauce be just as good? And if his applesauce was good, why not his apple jelly?

He was not one to stand and dream. The first thing you know he had not a building but a factory, with a half dozen of the best cooks he could hire cooking in his kitchens and scores of workers packing and shipping everywhere the apple cider and apple butter and applesauce and apple jelly made from the golden apples of all men's desire—for that is how he labeled all his products.

He owned farms all over the county and had planted his apple trees on all of them. He would let no apples from any other trees but his own be used in any of the foods he sold. He had strong feelings about this. His trees might not bear the golden apples of his brother's desire, he told himself, but they bore a golden stream for him. There seemed no end to what he could make out of an apple.

He preserved them and dried them and made juice out of them and turned them into jams and syrups and spun them into confections and distilled them into essences and blew them into fragrances. He made candy out of them—kinds no one had ever thought of before. He made a candy kiss—a puff of egg white and sugar and grated apple—that everybody said was the best-tasting candy they had ever tasted until he made an appy-taffle that everybody immediately said was even better.

His workers ate lunch with him every day so that he could try out all the new things his cooks were concocting. Everybody who ate the lunch said it was so good there ought to be a restaurant. So he opened a restaurant.

He started with a counter and four tables. Soon he needed more room, so he built a restaurant with thirty tables. Soon he needed more room than this.

He decided to build the fanciest restaurant he could build.

He hired a famous architect to build a restaurant with four great dining rooms, each different inside but each shaped outside like a golden apple.

He hired the world's greatest sign painter to create a perfect replica of an apple tree, to be installed on the roof. It had green leaves that rustled in the wind and looked so much like an apple tree that birds flew down and tried to eat its golden apples.

At night it was like no other apple tree on earth. Then its leaves glowed with a faint green phosphorescence and its apples turned to globes of golden light.

Under the apple tree neon letters two feet high continually spelled out:

THE INN OF THE GOLDEN APPLE

and under that in somewhat smaller letters:

of All Men's Desire

People came from everywhere to eat in the restaurant. Travelers drove hundreds of miles out of their way. And they told one another they were glad they had.

The food was like food nowhere else. Every dish was different and every dish was good. They roasted the chicken over apple wood. "It gives it a special flavor, don't you think?" said the brother. They served it with sauces whose ingredients no one could figure out but everyone licked up.

The dressing had a savor of apples, but it also had a subtlety of oysters and a whisper of chestnuts and some even said a suggestion of sage. But what was really in it no one knew.

There were dishes too numerous to describe. But no one ever ate in the restaurant and forgot the apple fritters. These looked as if they had been made out of the hole of a doughnut, and they were as light as if that was what they consisted of. They melted when they touched your palate and left not so much a taste as a memory.

And the desserts! There were a dozen of these. Regular customers who knew what they all tasted like sometimes went mad trying to choose just one. But most popular of all was the apple dumpling.

The apple dumpling came to the table steaming under a heavy mound of thick whipped cream. People who ate it argued as to whether it was a fruit or a confection, a syrup or a pastry, although some said it was an illusion, a conjurer's creation rather than a cook's, and you only imagined you were eating it. But most people, licking their lips and rubbing their bellies, believed that it was real enough.

It was as crumbly as a young girl's will, as spicy as a young man's wit, as sweet as a lover's note, as melting as a lover's heart. It was as syrupy as a soap opera, as buttery as a Sunday sermon, as juicy as a gossip's tale, as light as a politician's promises. Even after a meal that was much more than you should have eaten, it made you hungry all over again just to look at it and smell it, and once you tasted it, you could not stop until you had swallowed every savory drop and scraped the sides of the dish with your spoon.

The night the restaurant opened, a senator ate there and the governor of the state sent his regrets, which were probably genuine—he really was sorry he was not eating there. At once there was a steady stream of customers. The restaurant, like everything else the younger brother turned his hand to, was a success.

But what had happened to the older brother? The younger brother often wondered.

For the first year after he had left, letters had come, and for several years after that, post cards, all from faraway places—Tashkent and Budapest, Zanzibar and Azerbaijan, Ceylon and Tasmania. After that, no word had come at all.

Five years passed. Ten years. Twenty years. Twenty-five years. The younger man had long before given up all hope of ever hearing from the other again when one day an airmail letter arrived. The letter was from Tibet.

He opened it.

"Dear brother: I've found it! The golden apple of all

men's desire. Home Friday, bringing the apple. Can you meet me at the airport? Flight 437."

The younger brother could hardly wait till Friday came, and he was at the airport an hour ahead of time. He wondered if he would recognize his brother, but he recognized him the moment he came through the gate. And the older brother recognized him.

Immediately all the old love that had been there so many years before welled up. They threw their arms around one another.

"Where's the apple? I can't wait to see it," said the younger brother.

"I'll show it to you," said the other. "But first let's go home. I can't wait to get home again."

They drove home.

They came to the beautiful restaurant shaped like four golden apples with a perfect apple tree on top and the neon sign that blinked in two-foot letters:

THE INN OF THE GOLDEN APPLE

of All Men's Desire

In the distance were all the factories and warehouses and barns and parking lots and trucks. The older brother asked:

"What's all this?"

"I've been pretty successful," said the younger brother. "I've sold a lot of apples."

"You must have," said the older brother. "I never dreamed I'd find anything here like this."

"But now," said the younger brother, "I want to see what I know is truly the perfect apple."

"You will, you will," said the older brother. He unlocked

his suitcase and took from it a large block of transparent plastic. The younger brother saw that there was an apple embedded in this plastic. He turned the block over in his hands.

"How do I take it out?"

"Oh, you can't do that," said the older brother. "I've had it preserved in formaldehyde and sealed in plastic. It was the only way I could keep it perfect.

"I found it in a desolate valley in the desolate mountains of Tibet. I came on it at sundown. I recognized it at once as the tree of my dreams. A tree of perfect shape, each leaf perfect, each apple perfect. Unmarred by any blemish. Untouched by any bug. At first I thought I wouldn't dare pick one of the apples. But at last I did. I picked this one. Thank God I did. That night a bitter wind blew down from the mountaintop. The temperature, which had been much too warm for that time and that place, dropped far below freezing. When I woke in the morning, the tree was a blackened, wilted ruin. The sudden freeze had killed it. I stayed until I was sure, but there was no question. The tree was dead. As soon as I could, I packed my apple as you see it here and came home."

The younger brother could see that it was a beautiful apple. Its shape, its color, the texture of its skin, were exquisitely unlike anything he had ever seen before.

"It is perfect," he thought.

Some of his own apples were lying on the table nearby. They had never before looked so small and scraggly.

"There is no doubt," he said to his brother, looking at him proudly, "you have found the apple you were searching for, the golden apple of all men's desire. What did it taste like?"

"Taste like? Naturally I didn't taste it. That would have ruined it."

The other brother made no comment but said it was time to go to dinner. They walked over to the restaurant. After the meal, they walked back through the lobby. Along the counters were heaped all the delicious foods the younger brother made from his apples—the golden cider and ruby jelly and nut-brown butter and green-gold sauce, the many different kinds of candy, the frozen pies, the popovers, the turnovers, the dumplings, the ice cream. It took a counter forty feet long to hold them all.

There were even candied apples, glazed with a special syrup for the children. "They're different from anything you've ever eaten," said the younger brother. "Our own formula. Try one tomorrow."

As they walked across the parking lot, they heard a man getting into his car saying, "That was the best meal I ever ate in my life."

"And have you ever drunk such cider!" said the woman with him.

As they passed him, the man spoke to them: "They call this place the Inn of the Golden Apple of All Men's Desire, and they have a right to, don't they?"

"I hope so," said the younger brother.

When they reached the house, he said, "You probably want to get to bed. I know I do. I have to be up early in the morning. The head of my laboratory-kitchen wants me to taste a new apple delight they've just perfected."

The two men fell asleep as soon as they were in bed, but they dreamed. They dreamed about apple trees.

The trees the younger brother dreamed of had the most beautiful apples he had ever seen. They looked like the one his brother had brought. But when he tried to pick an apple, it was always somehow just beyond his reach, and he heard a voice saying, "This is the golden apple of all men's desire."

The tree the older brother dreamed of was a plain little tree with plain little apples on it, just like the ones his brother grew. But when he tried to pick an apple, it always somehow turned into something else, and he heard a voice saying, "This is the golden apple of all men's desire."

The dream woke the brothers. For a while they lay awake, feeling strangely disturbed. Through the windows they could see the beautiful apple tree on top of the inn, its leaves a soft phosphorescent green, its apples golden globes of light. The neon sign was still flashing off and on.

Soon they fell asleep again, and slept soundly.

Life will not let your dreams stay dead

Do you have dreams?

And have you let them die? Did you prick your finger on the facts of life and draw back into your dream?

Life will not let your dreams stay dead.

Have you ever thought how life grows?

Go out on a winter day and look at the branch of a tree. The bare branch is flawed with small scars.

Each scar marks where a leaf died.

But each scar marks where new life has formed.

Under the scar a new branch is hidden, and from its scars the tree will grow again.

If you have lived through many seasons, you, too, have scars. But you are not less for your scars; you are more. If they mark your losses, they also show your power to grow.

Do not sorrow for the life that has ended; from its scars comes forth the life that is to be.

The bare, scarred winter branches hide the green and growing woods of spring.

Life cries to the seed, "Grow!"

Life cries to the sleeper, "Wake!"

Life cries to him who is dead, "Come forth and live!"

You must never give up

In Florida they build islands. Into the bay they dump a truckload of sand. It is swallowed up. They dump another truckload. It, too, is swallowed up. They dump a hundred truckloads, and all of them are swallowed up. But they keep dumping sand, truckload by truckload, and after a while, an island begins to emerge!

We have to keep on, and we have to keep on when we feel like giving up.

We all have times when more is asked of us than we seem capable of giving.

But has the human story ever been more than a man—or a woman—coming up against something that barred his way, something that had written all over it, "Impassable, road closed, no trespassing, detour"—and the man said, "Perhaps, but I have to find out," and he went ahead.

You never know till you ask. You never find out till you press ahead.

For a chick to be born, it has to break its shell. Imagine how hard that must be!

But beyond the broken shell lies life—bursting out of limitations, starting on new ways of growth.

It is time for a breaking of shells.

In the last seventy-five years man has learned to fly and to send his voice around the earth; he has learned to see in the dark and to hear under the sea; he has unlocked the power in the atom; he has taken pictures of Mars and circled the moon; he has doubled his life span and banished scores of diseases.

If we could go back seventy-five years and ask if it were possible for men to do the things men have done, we would find scarcely a single person who would answer that it was possible.

We live in a miraculous moment. What miracle will you dare to say it does not hold?

Every single one of man's achievements, every single blessing we enjoy, we enjoy only because someone, when he came to the "Impassable" sign, said, "Perhaps, but I have to find out."

Someone refused to settle for what seems to be. Someone refused to accept the obvious limitation. Someone knocked at the door that opens on nowhere.

There are no immovable obstacles. There are only obstacles no one yet has moved. There are no insoluble problems. There are only problems no one yet has solved.

A small flower, the snowdrop, sends its green leaves up through a snowbank and opens its delicate blossom to hang in the ice-cold air. How dare such fragile petals have faith in spring when all the rest of us keep hugging winter to our wool-clad bones!

You walk on faith

Everyone fails, but everyone is not a failure.

Do not give up when things take a downward turn.

You can hold on for ten more minutes. You can take one step more.

It is like walking through a fog or a forest. You look, but all you see is mist and trees. You feel they will never end. Then, with the next step, you see the clearing.

When I was a boy, I used to love to hike into the country. Sometimes I walked too far and overjudged the distance I had to go. On one such occasion, night had fallen while I was still far from home. By the time I reached the bridge that led to town, fog had come down with the dark.

Now I stood before the bridge.

It was a long vehicular bridge across the river, with a catwalk for pedestrians at the side.

I hesitated.

Far below me, I knew there was the water that I could not see. Before me I knew there stretched the bridge, but now it was swallowed up in the foggy night. Under my feet the iron grille I strode on was invisible. The railing that I clutched disappeared in front of my hand.

I was frightened, but it was damp and cold and I was

hungry and tired. If I wanted to get home that night, I had to cross that bridge.

Gingerly I inched my foot forward, and shuffling step by step, sliding my hand along the rail, hardly daring to let go even to take a new grip, I walked out into the blackness of space, on the nothing I had faith was there, and crossed the river.

It was many years later that I realized that this is what we do all our life.

It is not the street that bears us up as we walk—it is faith.

Without faith, who can stand—let alone walk?

With faith, what road do we not dare to take?

Having faith, one walked on water.

Having faith, some walk on air and circumnavigate the heavens.

Every step a man takes is a venture in uncertainty—but when we step on faith, we step as on a rock of reassurance.

We walk as if God had us by the hand, and our life is a journey into jubilance.

Walk on faith.

Morning has been all night coming

How long has it been since you rose up with morning?

Morning has been all night coming.

At first, all you have is a sense of darkness thinning. Black is not so black; there is an indefinable paling.

Then there comes a streaking of the clouds low in the east. The sky is no longer everywhere the same.

Treetops catch morning first; they stand out clearly. Then the streaks in the eastern sky turn softly pink. Slowly, very slowly, color comes back to things.

You sense how many things have been looking for the light.

The birds begin to sing.

But morning makes no sound. You have to do the singing, like the birds.

Morning has been all night coming.

But see how certainly it comes.